# Tennis Trivia Quiz Book

## 500 Questions on the Kings and Queens of the Court

Chris Bradshaw

For rights and permissions, please contact:
C_D_Bradshaw@hotmail.com

ISBN-13: 978-1-7392137-2-5

Front cover image created by headfuzz by grimboid. Check out his great collection of TV, movie and sport-themed posters online at:

https://www.etsy.com/shop/headfuzzbygrimboid

# Introduction

Know your lobs from your drop shots? Your Nadals from your Navratilovas? Put your tennis knowledge to the test with this bumper collection of quizzes on the kings and queens of the court.

The Tennis Trivia Quiz Book covers all aspects of the game including Wimbledon, the Australian Open, the French Open and the U.S. Open as well as the Davis Cup, the Billie Jean King Cup and much else besides.

The biggest names in the history of the game are present and correct so look out for questions on Roger Federer, Serena Williams, Novak Djokovic, Steffi Graf, Andy Murray, Carlos Alcaraz and many, many more.

There are 500 questions in total covering all the big tournaments and the top players from both the men's and women's games.

Each quiz contains a selection of 20 questions and is either a mixed bag of pot luck testers or is centred on a specific category such as the Firsts and Lasts or All-Time Greats.

There are easy, medium and hard questions offering something for tennis novices as well as professors of the game.

You'll find the answers to each quiz below the bottom of the following quiz. For example, the answers to Quiz 1: Pot Luck, are underneath Quiz 2: Wimbledon Men's Singles. The only exception is Quiz 25: Pot Luck. The answers to these can be found under the Quiz 1 questions.

A quick note about terminology. I have used both Grand Slam and Major when referring to Wimbledon, the French Open, the U.S. Open and the Australian Open.

Records and statistics are accurate up to March 2023.

We'll open serve with some pot luck questions.

## About the Author

Chris Bradshaw has written 30 quiz books including titles for Britain's biggest selling daily newspaper, The Sun, and The Times (of London). In addition to the NFL, he has written extensively on soccer, cricket, darts and poker.

He lives in Birmingham, England and has been following tennis for over 30 years.

## Acknowledgements

Many thanks to Ken and Veronica Bradshaw, Heidi Grant, Steph, James, Ben and Will Roe, Graham Nash and Bill Rankin.

# CONTENTS


| | | |
|---|---|---|
| 1 | Pot Luck | 8 |
| 2 | Wimbledon Men's Singles | 10 |
| 3 | Pot Luck | 12 |
| 4 | Wimbledon Ladies' Singles | 14 |
| 5 | Pot Luck | 16 |
| 6 | Australian Open | 18 |
| 7 | Pot Luck | 20 |
| 8 | French Open | 22 |
| 9 | Pot Luck | 24 |
| 10 | U.S. Open | 26 |
| 11 | Pot Luck | 28 |
| 12 | All-Time Greats (Men) | 30 |
| 13 | Pot Luck | 32 |
| 14 | All-Time Greats (Women) | 34 |
| 15 | Pot Luck | 36 |

| | | |
|---|---|---|
| 16 | The Davis Cup | 38 |
| 17 | Pot Luck | 40 |
| 18 | The Billie Jean King Cup (Fed Cup) | 42 |
| 19 | Pot Luck | 44 |
| 20 | Wimbledon Firsts and Lasts | 46 |
| 21 | Pot Luck | 48 |
| 22 | Anagrams (Men) | 50 |
| 23 | Pot Luck | 52 |
| 24 | Anagrams (Women) | 54 |
| 25 | Pot Luck | 56 |

## Quiz 1: Pot Luck

1. The Wimbledon Championships start in which month?

2. Flushing Meadows is the setting for which Major?

3. Which player has earned the most prize money in the history of the ATP Tour?

4. A tie-break takes place if both players win how many games?

5. The winner of which Championship receives a trophy called The Musketeers' Cup?

6. What is the oldest of the four tennis Majors?

7. What is the name of the international team tournament made up of mixed gender teams?

8. What word is used to describe a serve that is not touched by the opposing player?

9. Who was the last British man before Andy Murray to reach a Major final?

10. True or false – Roger Federer is the father of two pairs of twins?

11. 'Pistol' was the nickname of which all-time great?

12. How many matches does a player have to win to be crowned the singles champion of a Grand Slam tournament?

13. Which Hollywood superstar played Richard Williams, father of Venus and Serena, in the 2021 movie drama 'King Richard'?

14. Which Major champion helped the rescue effort following a fire at a hotel in Rome in 2004?

15. True or false – The first edition of the Australian Open was hosted at a cricket ground?

16. Despite neither winning Wimbledon, who were the two players to win a record seven Men's Singles Majors during the 1980s?

17. In what decade did ball girls make their debut at Wimbledon?

18. The ATP's Sportsmanship Award is named after which Swedish great?

19. In what city was Andy Murray born? a) Dundee b) Edinburgh c) Glasgow

20. In what year was tennis reintroduced to the Olympic Games? a) 1984 b) 1988 c) 1992

## Quiz 25: Answers

1. Women's Singles at the Australian Open 2. The Laver Cup 3. Mark Edmondson 4. Andy Murray and Greg Rusedski 5. Tim Henman 6. Jimmy Connors and Roger Federer 7. Novak Djokovic 8. Steffi Graf 9. Greece 10. True 11. Right 12. Argentina 13. True 14. Yevgeny Kafelnikov 15. Pete Sampras 16. John McEnroe 17. The Lloyds (John, David and Tony) 18. True 19. c) 24 finals 20. c) 148mph

## Quiz 2: Wimbledon Men's Singles

1. Who holds the record for the most Wimbledon Men's Single's Championship wins?

2. Who is the youngest winner of the Wimbledon Men's Singles title?

3. In 2001, who became just the second unseeded player to win the Men's Singles at Wimbledon?

4. Andy Murray secured his first Men's Singles title in 2013 after beating which opponent in the final?

5. Murray added a second Men's Singles crown in 2016 after defeating which opponent?

6. Who was the last player to be match point down to go on and win the Men's Singles Final?

7. Roger Federer won the final set 16-14 in the 2009 Men's Singles Final to defeat which opponent?

8. Bjorn Borg was the first Swede to win the Men's Singles at Wimbledon. Who was the second?

9. Who holds the record for the most Wimbledon Men's Singles Championship wins by a left-handed player?

10. Who won seven Men's Singles titles between 1993 and 2000?

11. Which player interrupted that streak after winning the Men's Singles crown in 1996?

12. Prior to 2022, who was the last non-European to win the Men's Singles at Wimbledon?

13. Who was the first player in the open era to win the Wimbledon Men's Singles title without dropping a set?

14. Before Andy Murray, who was the last British player to win the Men's Singles at Wimbledon?

15. Who became the first player to climb up to the Players' Box after winning the 1987 Men's Singles title?

16. Boris Becker is one of two Germans to win the Wimbledon Men's Singles title. Who is the other?

17. Which opponent did John McEnroe defeat to secure his first Wimbledon Men's Singles title?

18. Lasting some 4hr 57min, the longest Men's Singles final in the history of Wimbledon was contested in 2019 by which pair?

19. What is the record for the most sets lost by a player who went on to win the Wimbledon Men's Singles? a) seven b) eight c) nine

20. The longest match ever played at Wimbledon lasted how many games? a) 181 b) 182 c) 183

## Quiz 1: Answers

1. June 2. U.S. Open 3. Novak Djokovic 4. Six 5. French Open Men's Singles 6. Wimbledon 7. The Hopman Cup 8. An ace 9. Greg Rusedski 10. True 11. Pete Sampras 12. Seven 13. Will Smith 14. Andy Roddick 15. True 16. Ivan Lendl and Mats Wilander 17. 1970s 18. Stefan Edberg 19. c) Glasgow 20. b) 1988

## Quiz 3: Pot Luck

1. Who holds the record for appearing in the most matches in the Ladies' Singles at Wimbledon?

2. The opening event on the ATP Tour calendar is hosted in which country?

3. Who was the runner-up in the Australian Open Men's Singles five times between 2010 and 2016?

4. In 1938, which American became the first man to win all four Majors in the same year?

5. What was the only Major not to take place during the covid-interrupted 2020 season?

6. Who won a combined 11 Men's Singles titles at Wimbledon and the French Open by the time he was just 25?

7. Whose 15 Men's Singles Major wins during the 2000s were the most by any player that decade?

8. True or false – Bjorn Borg's career at the Australian Open consisted of just two matches?

9. Who was the first man born in the 2000s to win a Grand Slam singles title?

10. Which Hollywood star played John McEnroe in the hit 2017 movie 'Borg vs. McEnroe'?

11. Casper Ruud was the first man from which country to win an ATP Tour title and appear in a Major final?

12. The Norman Brookes Challenge Cup is awarded to the winner of which tournament?

13. 'The Scud' was the nickname of which big-serving Australian?

14. Who is Steffi Graf's tennis-playing husband?

15. At the Australian Open, play can be suspended if the temperature tops which figure?

16. In what decade was Wimbledon broadcast on television for the first time?

17. Which veteran Italian won the Woman's Singles at the U.S. Open in 2015 then immediately announced her retirement?

18. Which American's 56 indoor tournament victories are the most by a male player in the open era?

19. Andy Murray had surgery on what part of his body in both 2018 and 2019? a) hip b) knee c) shoulder

20. Between 1976 and 1981 Bjorn Borg won how many consecutive matches in the Men's Singles at Wimbledon? a) 37 b) 41 c) 45

**Quiz 2: Answers**

1. Roger Federer 2. Boris Becker 3. Goran Ivanisevic 4. Novak Djokovic 5. Milos Raonic 6. Novak Djokovic 7. Andy Roddick 8. Stefan Edberg 9. Rod Laver 10. Pete Sampras 11. Richard Krajicek 12. Lleyton Hewitt 13. Bjorn Borg 14. Fred Perry 15. Pat Cash 16. Michael Stich 17. Bjorn Borg 18. Novak Djokovic and Roger Federer 19. b) Eight 20. c) 183 games

## Quiz 4: Wimbledon Ladies' Singles Championship

1. Who holds the record for the most Wimbledon Ladies' Singles Championship wins?

2. 2022 winner Elena Rybakina was the first player to win the Ladies' Singles representing which country?

3. Who has won more Wimbledon Ladies' Singles titles – Serena or Venus Williams?

4. Martina Navratilova was the first Czech-born player to win the Wimbledon Ladies' Singles Championship. Who was the second?

5. The longest ever Ladies' Singles final took place in 2005 and lasted 2 hours 46 minutes. Which two Americans were playing?

6. True or false – Up to the 2022 championship, no unseeded player had won the Wimbledon Ladies' Singles?

7. Who was the last player to win the Ladies' Singles at Wimbledon while wearing glasses?

8. Who holds the record for serving the most aces in a single game in a Ladies' Singles match at Wimbledon?

9. In 1997, which 16-year-old became the youngest Ladies' Singles winner of the open era?

10. Up to and including the 2022 Championship, who was the last woman to win the Ladies' Singles title in back-to-back years?

11. Since 2000, who are the two Frenchwomen to win the Ladies' Singles at Wimbledon?

12. Which woman won 50 straight matches in the Ladies' Singles in the 1920s and 1930s?

13. In 1990, which 14-year-old became the youngest player to take part in the Ladies' Singles Championship?

14. 2017 Ladies' Singles champion Garbiñe Muguruza was born in which South American country?

15. Whose 24 successive appearances in the Wimbledon Ladies' Singles are the most in the history of the Championships?

16. In 2013, who became the most recent player to win the Ladies' Singles without dropping a set?

17. Which Wimbledon Ladies' Singles champion played for the Brisbane Heat in cricket's Women's Big Bash League?

18. In 1993, three sisters from which family were all seeded in the Ladies' Singles Championship?

19. Who holds the record for the most successive Ladies' Singles Championship wins in the open era? a) Steffi Graf b) Martina Navratilova c) Serena Williams

20. The fastest serve in the history of the Ladies' Singles at Wimbledon of 129mph in 2009 was recorded by which player? a) Maria Sharapova b) Serena Williams c) Venus Williams

**Quiz 3: Answers**

1. Martina Navratilova 2. Australia 3. Andy Murray 4. Don Budge 5. Wimbledon 6. Bjorn Borg 7. Roger Federer 8. True 9. Carlos Alcaraz 10. Shia LaBeouf 11. Norway 12. Men's Singles at the Australian Open 13. Mark Philippoussis 14. Andre Agassi 15. 40C or 104F 16. 1930s 17. Flavia Pennetta 18. Jimmy Connors 19. a) hip 20. b) 41 matches

## Quiz 5: Pot Luck

1. Who is the youngest player to reach #1 in the end of year ATP Men's World Rankings?

2. In 1953, who became the first woman to win all four Majors in the same season?

3. Which player has defeated Roger Federer the most times in singles matches?

4. There's a court at Flushing Meadows named after which jazz musician?

5. Which brothers won Men's Doubles titles at Wimbledon in 2006, 2011 and 2013?

6. Which all-time great won the most Major Men's Singles titles during the 1970s?

7. Who are the three women to have won more than $1 million in prize money before their 17th birthday?

8. In what year were final set tie-breaks introduced at Wimbledon?

9. Amazingly, it took until 2020 for the first player born in the 1990s to win a men's singles Major. Who won that U.S. Open title?

10. What is the only Grand Slam tournament that has been hosted in more than one country?

11. Which controversial character reached his first Grand Slam singles final at Wimbledon in 2022?

12. In February 2023, who became the first American man in almost 14 years to be ranked in the top 5 in the ATP World Rankings?

13. Who was the previous American man to reach the top 5?

14. 'You cannot be serious' is a phrase associated with which player?

15. In 1998, who became the second Czech player to win the Men's Singles at the Australian Open?

16. Who is the oldest player to be ranked #1 in the Men's ATP World Rankings?

17. Who is the only male tennis player to have been awarded the U.S. Presidential Medal of Honor?

18. What was the only Major that wasn't interrupted by World War I or World War II?

19. With 109 titles, who has the most career wins in the open era? a) Jimmy Connors b) Roger Federer c) Ivan Lendl

20. Approximately how many tennis balls are used during the Wimbledon Championships? a) 33,000 b) 43,000 c) 53,000

**Quiz 4: Answers**

1. Martina Navratilova 2. Kazakhstan 3. Serena Williams 4. Jana Novotna 5. Venus Williams and Lindsay Davenport 6. True 7. Martina Navratilova 8. Serena Williams 9. Martina Hingis 10. Serena Williams 11. Amelie Mauresmo and Marion Bartoli 12. Helen Wills-Moody 13. Jennifer Capriati 14. Venezuela 15. Virginia Wade 16. Marion Bartoli 17. Ash Barty 18. Maleeva 19. b) Martina Navratilova 20. c) Venus Williams

## Quiz 6: Australian Open

1. Who has won the Australian Open Men's Singles title the most times?

2. Which Belarusian claimed her first Grand Slam singles title after winning the 2023 Australian Open?

3. In 1995, who became the first (and so far, only) player to win the Australian Open Men's Singles in his debut appearance?

4. With 11 singles titles between 1960 and 1973, who is the most successful female player in the history of the Australian Open?

5. In 2007, who became just the second unseeded player to win the Australian Open Women's Singles title?

6. In 1997, which 16-year-old became the youngest winner of a Grand Slam title after winning the Australian Open Women's Singles crown?

7. Between 2006 and 2023 every Australian Open Men's Singles title bar one was won by Federer, Nadal or Djokovic. Who won in 2014?

8. Which Aussie is the only unseeded player to win the Men's Singles at the Australian Open?

9. Who is both the oldest and youngest player to win the Australian Open Men's Singles title?

10. The Australian Open is hosted in which city?

11. True or false – Until 1987, the Australian Open was played on grass?

12. Who was the last woman to successfully defend the Australian Open Women's Singles title?

13. Who was the last teenager to win the Australian Open Men's Singles title? (Clue: it was in 1985)

14. Andy Murray is one of two British players to reach the final of the Australian Open Men's Singles in the open era. Who is the other?

15. In 2014, who became the first Chinese woman to win the Women's Singles?

16. True or false – Neither Bjorn Borg nor John McEnroe won the Australian Open Men's Singles title?

17. Who won his first Australian Open title in 2009 then had to wait another 13 years to win his second?

18. Who are the two Germans to have won the Australian Open Women's Singles title?

19. The longest ever Grand Slam final was the 2012 Australian Open Men's Singles between Novak Djokovic and Roger Federer. How long did it last? a) 4h 53m b) 5h 53m c) 6h 53m

20. The 2023 Australian Open set an attendance record for a Grand Slam event after how many spectators went through the turnstiles? a) 639,192 b) 739,192 c) 839,192

## Quiz 5: Answers

1. Carlos Alcaraz 2. Maureen Connolly 3. Novak Djokovic 4. Louis Armstrong 5. Bob and Mike Bryan 6. Bjorn Borg 7. Martina Hingis, Jennifer Capriati and Monica Seles 8. 2019 9. Dominic Thiem 10. Australian Open which was twice hosted in New Zealand 11. Nick Kyriogos 12. Taylor Fritz 13. Andy Roddick 14. John McEnroe 15. Petr Korda 16. Roger Federer 17. Arthur Ashe 18. U.S. Open 19. a) Jimmy Connors 20. c) 53,000 balls

## Quiz 7: Pot Luck

1. 'Wild Thing' is the nickname of which controversial contemporary player?

2. With 63 tournament victories who has been the most successful clay court player on the ATP Tour in the open era?

3. Which Aussie was the first player to win all four Majors in the same season more than once?

4. Which opponent did Roger Federer face the most times throughout his career?

5. The courts at the U.S. Open are all what colour?

6. Who is the only woman who has had to qualify for a Major to go on and win that year's tournament?

7. Men's Singles matches at the four Majors are played over the best of how many sets?

8. Which woman completed the career Grand Slam after winning the 2012 French Open?

9. Born in Prague in 1921, which three-time Grand Slam winner was also an ice hockey star who represented four different countries during his tennis career?

10. At Wimbledon, tiebreakers take place in the final set when the scores reach how many games all?

11. Which Aussie was part of nine Wimbledon Men's Doubles-winning partnerships between 1993 and 2004?

12. Who is the only player to have won the Australian Open Men's Singles title on both grass and hard courts?

13. Who was the first Polish woman to win a Grand Slam singles tournament?

14. True or false – Up until 1961, a serving player had to keep at least one foot on the floor?

15. 'Fraulein Forehand' was the nickname of which great of the women's game?

16. In 2009, who became the first female tennis player to receive the U.S. Presidential Medal of Honor?

17. Who are the three Swedish players to have won the Men's Singles at the Australian Open?

18. Since 2006, officials at Wimbledon have worn uniforms created by which fashion designer?

19. How wide in feet is a doubles court? a) 34 feet b) 36 feet c) 38 feet

20. British U.S. Open winner Emma Raducanu was born in which city? a) Montreal b) Toronto c) Vancouver

**Quiz 6: Answers**

1. Novak Djokovic 2. Aryna Sabalenka 3. Andre Agassi 4. Margaret Court 5. Venus Williams 6. Martina Hingis 7. Stanislas Wawrinka 8. Mark Edmondson 9. Ken Rosewall 10. Melbourne 11. True 12. Victoria Azarenka 13. Stefan Edberg 14. John Lloyd 15. Li Na 16. True 17. Rafa Nadal 18. Steffi Graf and Angelique Kerber 19. b) 5h 53m 20. c) 839,192

## Quiz 8: French Open

1. Who won the Men's Singles for a record 14th time at the 2022 French Open?

2. The French Open is hosted at which Parisian venue?

3. Which Pole won the Women's Singles in both 2020 and 2022?

4. Aged just 16 years and 6 months, who is the youngest woman to win the Women's Singles at the French Open? (Clue: it was in 1990)

5. Which American won the Women's Singles title seven times between 1974 and 1986?

6. Between 2010 and 2022 every French Open Men's Singles title bar one was won by Nadal or Djokovic. Who won in 2015?

7. In 1989, who became the youngest player to win the Men's Singles at the French Open?

8. Which American won back-to-back Men's Singles titles in 1991 and 1992?

9. Who is the only Frenchman to have won the Men's Singles at the French Open in the open era?

10. Who was the last Frenchwoman to win the Women's Singles?

11. Prior to Rafa Nadal, who was the last player to win three straight Men's Singles titles?

12. True or false – Roger Federer has never won the French Open?

13. Since 2006 the French Open has started on what day of the week?

14. Which Swede was the first player to defeat Rafa Nadal in the French Open?

15. Who is the oldest man to win the Men's Singles title at the French Open?

16. Which Argentine, whose first name and surname start with the same letter, was the last unseeded player to win the French Open Men's Singles?

17. Who was the last woman to win three straight Women's Singles titles at the French Open?

18. The showpiece court at the French Open is named after which former player, journalist and administrator?

19. Which of the following players won the French Open Women's Singles the most times? a) Steffi Graf b) Justine Henin c) Monica Seles

20. Who was the first player to win the Men's Singles at the French Open in his debut appearance? a) Gustavo Kuerten b) Ivan Lendl c) Mats Wilander

## Quiz 7: Answers

1. Nick Kyrgios 2. Rafa Nadal 3. Rod Laver 4. Rafa Nadal 5. Blue 6. Emma Raducanu 7. Five sets 8. Maria Sharapova 9. Jaroslav Drobný 10. Six games all 11. Todd Woodbridge 12. Mats Wilander 13. Iga Swiatek 14. True 15. Steffi Graf 16. Billie Jean King 17. Stefan Edberg, Mats Wilander and Thomas Johansson 18. Ralph Lauren 19. b) 36 feet 20. b) Toronto

## Quiz 9: Pot Luck

1. What is the only Major that is played on clay courts?

2. What do the initials ATP stand for?

3. Which South American man tied a tour record in 1977 after winning 16 titles?

4. Who became the first Chinese man to win an ATP Tour event after winning the 2023 Abu Dhabi Open?

5. Which woman appeared in 13 straight Major finals from the 1987 French Open through to the 1990 French Open?

6. Which Australian did Roger Federer defeat in the final to claim his first Wimbledon title?

7. True or false – During the mid-1970s the U.S. Open was played on clay courts?

8. Who is the only man from the Netherlands to win a Grand Slam singles title?

9. Women's singles matches in the four Majors are played over the best of how many sets?

10. Which woman has the most career match wins in the history of Grand Slam singles tournaments?

11. Who was the first Danish player to win a Grand Slam singles title?

12. In 2019, who became the first player to win the Men's Singles final at Wimbledon via a final set tiebreak?

13. What colour are the courts at the Australian Open?

14. In 1982, which American became just the second player in Davis Cup history to play and win the maximum number of singles and doubles matches in a calendar year?

15. Who is the only player to complete the career Grand Slam and win Olympic Gold in both singles and doubles?

16. 'Boom Boom' was the nickname of which multiple Wimbledon winner?

17. 'Serious' was the title of which legendary player's autobiography?

18. Who was fined $10,000 after admitting spitting towards a spectator during a 2022 Wimbledon first-round match?

19. How long did the longest match at Wimbledon take to complete? a) 10 hours 5 minutes b) 11 hours 5 minutes c) 12 hours 5 minutes

20. Which player won that marathon Wimbledon encounter? a) Kevin Anderson b) John Isner c) Nicolas Mahut

**Quiz 8: Answers**

1. Rafa Nadal 2. Stade Roland-Garros 3. Iga Świątek 4. Monica Seles 5. Chris Evert 6. Stan Wawrinka 7. Michael Chang 8. Jim Courier 9. Yannick Noah 10. Mary Pierce 11. Bjorn Borg 12. False 13. Sunday 14. Robin Soderling 15. Rafa Nadal 16. Gaston Gaudio 17. Justine Henin 18. Philippe-Chatrier 19. a) Steffi Graf 20. c) Mats Wilander

## Quiz 10: U.S. Open

1. Who are the three men to have won the U.S. Open Men's Singles title five times in the open era?

2. Who are the two women with six U.S. Open Women's Singles titles in the open era?

3. The U.S. Open starts on the last Monday of which month?

4. The USTA National Center which hosts the U.S. Open is named after which legend of the game?

5. The finals of the U.S. Open are played on a court named after which player?

6. Which rising star claimed his first Major title after winning the 2022 U.S. Open Men's Singles?

7. In 1990, which legend of the game became the first teenager to win the Men's Singles at the U.S. Open?

8. In 2021, who became the second Russian to win the Men's Singles at the U.S. Open?

9. True or false – The total prize pool at the 2022 U.S. Open was more than $60 million?

10. In 1994, which star became the first unseeded player to win the U.S. Open Men's Singles title?

11. Who was the last American to win the Men's Singles at the U.S. Open?

12. In 2009, which Belgian became the first unseeded player to win the Women's Singles at the U.S. Open?

13. Who are the two Britons to have won the Women's Singles in the open era?

14. Aged just 16 years and 8 months, who is the youngest winner of the Women's Singles title at the U.S. Open? (clue: she won in 1979)

15. True or false – Up to 1974 the U.S. Open was played on grass?

16. Which Aussie won back-to-back Men's Singles titles in 1997 and 1998?

17. Who is the only player to have won the Women's Singles at the U.S. Open without dropping a set?

18. Which alliteratively named American won the Women's Singles title in 2017?

19. The grounds at the U.S. Open are home to how many competition courts? a) 20 b) 22 c) 24

20. Flushing Meadows, home of the U.S. National Tennis Center, is in which New York borough? a) Brooklyn b) Manhattan c) Queens

## Quiz 9: Answers

1. French Open 2. Association of Tennis Professionals 3. Guillermo Vilas 4. Yu Wibing 5. Steffi Graf 6. Mark Philippoussis 7. True 8. Richard Krajicek 9. Three 10. Serena Williams 11. Caroline Wozniacki 12. Novak Djokovic 13. Blue 14. John McEnroe 15. Serena Williams 16. Boris Becker 17. John McEnroe 18. Nick Kyrgios 19. b) 11 hours 5 minutes 20. b) John Isner

## Quiz 11: Pot Luck

1. Who is the only player given a Wild Card entry to go on to win the Men's Singles at Wimbledon?

2. Throughout the whole of his career Roger Federer used a racquet made by which manufacturer?

3. What do the initials WTA stand for?

4. Who was the last man to win three Majors in the same season?

5. Roger Federer won his final Wimbledon title in 2017. Which Croat did he defeat in the final?

6. Who reached a record eight straight Men's Singles finals at the U.S. Open between 1982 and 1989?

7. The governing body for tennis in Great Britain is the LTA. What do the initials LTA stand for?

8. In what decade were tiebreakers introduced at Wimbledon?

9. Who was the only American woman to win a Grand Slam singles title during the 1990s?

10. Who was the first Chinese player to win a Major singles title?

11. What was the last of the four Majors to introduce a final set tie break?

12. Whose 19 career titles on grass are the most by a male player on the ATP Tour?

13. True or false – Former NBA basketball star Joakim Noah is the son of the former tennis player Yannick Noah?

14. What was the last country to successfully defend the Davis Cup? (Clue: It was in 2012 and 2013)

15. Alongside Wimbledon, Venus Williams won a singles title in which other Major?

16. 'The King of Clay' is the nickname of which all-time great?

17. Who was stabbed by a crazed German man during a 1993 game in Hamburg?

18. Who was fined $17,000 after losing her cool with the umpire during the 2018 U.S. Open Final?

19. Which English seaside resort plays host to a grass court event in the run up to Wimbledon? a) Brighton b) Eastbourne c) Torquay

20. What is the most games played in a single set in the history of the Wimbledon Championships? a) 118 b) 128 c) 138

**Quiz 10: Answers**

1. Jimmy Connors, Pete Sampras and Roger Federer 2. Chris Evert and Serena Williams 3. August 4. Billie Jean King 5. Arthur Ashe 6. Carlos Alcaraz 7. Pete Sampras 8. Daniil Medvedev 9. True 10. Andre Agassi 11. Andy Roddick 12. Kim Clijsters 13. Virginia Wade and Emma Raducanu 14. Tracy Austin 15. True 16. Pat Rafter 17. Emma Raducanu 18. Sloane Stephens 19. b) 22 courts 20. c) Queens

## Quiz 12: All-Time Greats – Men

1. Novak Djokovic is from which country?

2. Who is the only man to achieve 100 match wins at Wimbledon?

3. Which multiple Major winner refused to shave as long as he was still in the tournament at Wimbledon?

4. Who holds the record for the most Major singles championship wins by an American player?

5. Which future champion did Andre Agassi defeat at Wimbledon in 1992 to claim his first major title?

6. Who was the first black player to win the Men's Singles at Wimbledon, the Australian Open and the U.S. Open?

7. Who is the only player to appear in ten straight Major finals?

8. Who is the only man to simultaneously be ranked the world #1 in both singles and doubles?

9. Which player's career CV includes five U.S. Opens, one Australian Open and two Wimbledon singles titles as well as a 160-week run as the world number 1?

10. Which American, who won Wimbledon and the U.S. Open in the early 70s, gives his name to a hugely popular style of Adidas sneakers?

11. Rafa Nadal secured his first Wimbledon Men's Singles title in 2008 after defeating which opponent?

12. Whose four Major singles titles in the 1970s are the most ever by an Argentine player?

13. Andy Murray secured gold at the 2012 London Olympics after beating which legend in the final?

14. Which eight-time Major winner later became a coach, helping Andy Murray to multiple Grand Slam titles?

15. Whose run of 911 consecutive weeks in the top 10 in the ATP World Rankings is the longest such streak in the history of the game?

16. Who is the only Brazilian to have won a Major singles title?

17. What was the only Major that Boris Becker failed to win?

18. Boris Becker, Jimmy Connors and Roger Federer were all beaten in the final of Wimbledon how many times?

19. What is Andy Murray's hometown? a) Dumbarton b) Dunblane c) Dundee

20. Rafa Nadal is from which Spanish island? a) Lanzarote b) Mallorca c) Tenerife

**Quiz 11: Answers**

1. Goran Ivanisevic 2. Wilson 3. Women's Tennis Association 4. Novak Djokovic 5. Marin Čilić 6. Ivan Lendl 7. Lawn Tennis Association 8. 1970s 9. Lindsay Davenport 10. Li Na 11. French Open 12. Roger Federer 13. True 14. Czech Republic 15. U.S. Open 16. Rafa Nadal 17. Monica Seles 18. Serena Williams 19. b) Eastbourne 20. c) 138 games

## Quiz 13: Pot Luck

1. Which legend of the game appeared in 31 Wimbledon Championships from the 1970s through to the 2000s?

2. As well as being the home of the All-England Lawn Tennis Club, what other sport has its headquarters at Wimbledon?

3. Which man holds the record for the longest consecutive spell as the ATP's World #1 ranked player?

4. What was the first of the four Grand Slam events to host an open tournament?

5. In what month does the French Open usually begin?

6. Which opponent did Roger Federer defeat in the 2004, 2005 and 2009 Wimbledon finals?

7. Johan Kriek is the only man from which country to win a Major singles title in the open era?

8. Who is the only man to have won the Queen's Club Tournament five times?

9. Final set tie breakers in Majors are the first to how many points (with an advantage of two points)?

10. The ITF Hall of Fame is located in which country?

11. Which Frenchman was the last man to win a Grand Slam singles title using a wooden racket?

12. Which European country won six Davis Cup titles between 1984 and 1998?

13. According to Forbes magazines, who is the highest earning sportswoman of all time?

14. Who won a record 43 straight matches and seven consecutive titles across the 2010 and 2011 seasons?

15. 'Rusty' was the nickname of which Australian star?

16. What is the name of the Netflix documentary series that offers viewers a behind the scenes look at life on tour?

17. Up to the start of the 2023 season, who was the last man to win a Major who comes from a country that doesn't have red in its flag? (Clue: he's a South American)

18. Which player, who shares a name with a former England cricket all-rounder, was beaten by John McEnroe in the 1983 Wimbledon Men's Singles final?

19. How wide is a tennis court for a singles match? a) 25 feet b) 26 feet c) 27 feet

20. Up to the start of the 2023 season, how many men had completed the career Grand Slam? a) seven b) eight c) nine

## Quiz 12: Answers

1. Serbia 2. Roger Federer 3. Bjorn Borg 4. Pete Sampras 5. Goran Ivanisevic 6. Arthur Ashe 7. Roger Federer 8. John McEnroe 9. Jimmy Connors 10. Stan Smith 11. Roger Federer 12. Guillermo Vilas 13. Roger Federer 14. Ivan Lendl 15. Rafa Nadal 16. Gustavo Kuerten 17. French Open 18. Four times 19. b) Dunblane 20. b) Mallorca

## Quiz 14: All-Time Greats – Women

1. Whose 167 career singles titles are the most in the history of the women's game?

2. Whose 23 singles Major wins are the most by a woman in the open era?

3. Which Belgian woman won seven Major singles titles between 2003 and 2007?

4. Who is the only woman to appear in more than 90 Grand Slam singles tournaments?

5. Who holds the record for spending the most weeks at number one in the WTA World Rankings?

6. Who famously routed Bobby Riggs in the contest dubbed 'The Battle of the Sexes'?

7. Who was the first woman to top the $1 million mark in career prize money?

8. Who is the only woman to have won both the French Open and the Australian Open three times in a row? (Clue: it was in the 1990s)

9. Who is the youngest woman to win a WTA Singles event? She won the Portland title in 1977 aged just 14.

10. Best known for her exploits on clay, who was the first Spaniard to win the Women's Singles at the U.S. Open?

11. Who was the first Russian woman to win more than one Major singles title?

12. In 1970, who became the first woman in the open era to complete the Grand Slam by winning all four Majors in the same year?

13. Who was the second woman in the open era to complete a Grand Slam, this time in 1988?

14. Who is the youngest player to reach the number one position in the WTA World Rankings?

15. Known for remaining cool under pressure, which legend of the game was nicknamed 'The Ice Maiden'?

16. Whose 34 Major singles final appearances are the most by a woman in the open era?

17. Who was the first black player to win the U.S. Open, the French Open and Wimbledon?

18. Who are the two women to have spent a record 186 consecutive weeks as the World #1?

19. What was the only Major singles title missing from Martina Hingis's collection? a) Australian Open b) French Open c) U.S. Open

20. During the 1984 season Martina Navratilova set a record after winning how many consecutive matches? a) 54 b) 64 c) 74

**Quiz 13: Answers**

1. Martina Navratoliva 2. Croquet 3. Novak Djokovic 4. French Open 5. May 6. Andy Roddick 7. South Africa 8. Andy Murray 9. Ten points 10. USA 11. Yannick Noah 12. Sweden 13. Serena Williams 14. Novak Djokovic 15. Lleyton Hewitt 16. Break Point 17. Juan Martin del Potro 18. Chris Lewis 19. c) 27 feet 20. b) Eight

## Quiz 15: Pot Luck

1. The last Men's Singles final at Wimbledon made up of two players from the same country featured which pair?

2. What was special about the 2009 Wimbledon fourth round Ladies' Singles match between Amelie Mauresmo and Dinara Safina?

3. Which woman holds the record for most weeks as the WTA's #1 ranked doubles player?

4. Which future Grand Slam winner became the ATP's youngest champion at the 1998 Adelaide Open, aged just 16?

5. What was the only major that Pete Sampras failed to win?

6. Which famous name from the world of tennis was the first man to fly non-stop across the Mediterranean Sea?

7. Who was the only man to win three Majors in the same season during the 1980s?

8. Former Wimbledon and U.S. Open runner-up Kevin Anderson is from which country?

9. Who is the only player to win five straight U.S. Open Men's Singles titles?

10. Which Briton won her only Major singles title at the 1976 French Open?

11. Which Spaniard, who in 2023 became just the second man to appear in more than 80 Grand Slam singles tournaments, has never got past the quarter final in any of them?

12. Who was the first teenager to reach number one in the men's ATP World Rankings?

13. Which 20-year-old was the previous holder of the record for the youngest player to reach the ATP World Number 1? (Clue: It was in 2001)

14. 'Open' was the title of which multiple Major-winning star's critically acclaimed 2009 autobiography?

15. Introduced in 1909, what are the official colours of the All-England Lawn Tennis Club?

16. Who gave himself an impromptu mid-match haircut during a 2015 ATP Tour Finals contest against Rafa Nadal?

17. Which man won his first tour event in August 1970 and his last almost 25 years later in June 1995?

18. Who is the youngest player to have won the Men's Singles at a Major?

19. How old was he won he won that title? a) 16 b) 17 c) 18

20. What is the seating capacity of Centre Court at Wimbledon? a) 13,974 b) 14,974 c) 15,974

**Quiz 14: Answers**

1. Martina Navratilova 2. Serena Williams 3. Justine Henin 4. Venus Williams 5. Steffi Graf 6. Billie Jean King 7. Chris Evert 8. Monica Seles 9. Tracy Austin 10. Arantxa Sanchez-Vicario 11. Maria Sharapova 12. Margaret Court 13. Steffi Graf 14. Martina Hingis 15. Chris Evert 16. Chris Evert 17. Althea Gibson 18. Steffi Graf and Serena Williams 19. b) French Open 20. c) 74

## Quiz 16: The Davis Cup

1. Which country has won the Davis Cup the most times?

2. Which country won the Davis Cup for the first time in 2022?

3. They secured that maiden title by defeating which country in the final?

4. A Davis Cup contest is made up of how many matches?

5. How many countries took part in the Finals section of the 2022 Davis Cup?

6. In 2015, Britain won the Davis Cup for the first time since 1936 after defeating which country in the final?

7. What was the last country to win a Davis Cup final played on grass?

8. True or false – Andy Murray was a perfect 8-0 in matches during the 2015 Davis Cup?

9. What is the only South American country to have won the Davis Cup?

10. Since professionals were first allowed to play in 1972 which country's seven wins are the most in the Davis Cup by a European team?

11. Up to the start of the 2023 competition, which legend of the game had a winning streak of 32 matches in singles and doubles contests?

12. Since 2018, Davis Cup matches have been played over the best of how many sets?

13. True or false – Roger Federer never won the Davis Cup?

14. Which Cypriot Grand Slam finalist holds the record for the most consecutive singles wins in the Davis Cup with 36?

15. True or false – Dwight F. Davis, the founder of the competition, was a politician whose roles included the Governor of the Philippines and the United States Secretary of War?

16. Which country reached the final of the Davis Cup every year between 1946 and 1968?

17. The final stages of the 2022 Davis Cup were hosted in which southern Spanish city?

18. What was the first European country other than Great Britain to win the Davis Cup?

19. In what year was the first Davis Cup held? a) 1890 b) 1900 c) 1910

20. How many countries entered the 2023 Davis Cup? a) 135 b) 145 c) 155

**Quiz 15: Answers**

1. Pete Sampras and Andre Agassi 2. It was first played with the Centre Court roof closed 3. Martina Navratilova 4. Lleyton Hewitt 5. French Open 6. Roland Garros 7. Mats Wilander 8. South Africa 9. Roger Federer 10. Sue Barker 11. Feliciano Lopez 12. Carlos Alcaraz 13. Lleyton Hewitt 14. Andre Agassi 15. Dark green and purple 16. Andy Murray 17. Jimmy Connors 18. Michael Chang 19. b) 17 20. b) 14,974

## Quiz 17: Pot Luck

1. Who was the first unseeded player to win the Men's Singles at Wimbledon?

2. For more than a century the balls at Wimbledon have been made by which manufacturer?

3. When introduced in 1973 which larger than life character was the first man to be ranked the world's #1 player?

4. Which Frenchman, still active on tour in 2023, won his first ATP Tour match way back in 2002, aged just 15?

5. Which Grand Slam tournament winner was the long-time host of the BBC TV quiz show 'A Question of Sport'?

6. Who was the only man to win three Majors in the same season during the 1970s?

7. Which Indian tennis player appeared alongside Roger Moore in the 1983 James Bond film, 'Octopussy'?

8. Who is the only American man to have completed a career Grand Slam and won an Olympic gold medal?

9. Who holds the record for appearing in the most Men's Singles matches in the history of Wimbledon?

10. Who is the only woman to win a Grand Slam singles event every year for 13 straight years?

11. Who became the first woman born in the 2000s to win a Grand Slam singles event after claiming the 2019 U.S. Open title?

12. Who was the first woman to win a Major title using a metal racket?

13. Which winner of the Ladies' Singles at Wimbledon was the captain of Spain's Men's Davis Cup team from 2015 through to 2017?

14. 'The Punisher' was the nickname of which player?

15. In 2022, which 6ft 10in American set the record for serving the most career aces?

16. Which big-serving Croat was the previous holder of that aces record?

17. Which superstar wrote the 2013 book 'Seventy-Seven: My Road to Wimbledon Glory'?

18. The Aorangi Park practice courts are a feature of which famous tennis venue?

19. The first ever event in the open era of tennis was hosted in which English seaside resort? a) Bournemouth b) Bridlington c) Brighton

20. How long is a tennis court? a) 78 feet b) 79 feet c) 80 feet

**Quiz 16: Answers**

1. USA 2. Canada 3. Australia 4. Five 5. 16 countries 6. Belgium 7. Australia 8. True 9. Argentina 10. Sweden 11. Rafa Nadal 12. Three 13. False 14. Marcos Baghdatis 15. True 16. Australia 17. Malaga 18. France 19. b) 1900 20. c) 155 countries

## Quiz 18: Billie Jean King Cup (Formerly The Federation Cup)

Questions and answers in this round refer to the competition throughout its history, including when it was named the Federation Cup, Fed Cup and Billie Jean King Cup.

1. Which country has won the Billie Jean Cup the most times?

2. Which country won the trophy for the first time in 2022?

3. The 2022 final was hosted in which British city?

4. Which Spanish Major winner's 72 combined singles and doubles wins are the most in the history of the Billie Jean King Cup?

5. Which Australian great had a perfect 20-0 win/loss record in singles matches in this competition?

6. Which other legend of the game (who represented two countries) also has a perfect 20/0 singles record?

7. What was the last country to successfully defend the Billie Jean King Cup? (Clue: It was in 2015 and 2016)

8. Who are the two Americans to have won the Billie Jean King Cup as both a player and captain?

9. Which country won a record 37 straight ties between 1976 and 1983?

10. Ties in the Finals of the Billie Jean King Cup are played over the best of how many matches?

11. Which legend of the game is the oldest player to take part in a World Group match, appearing for the U.S. in 2004 at the age of 47?

12. Which country appeared in the final for eight straight years between 1973 and 1980?

13. True or false – Serena Williams never won a Billie Jean King Cup?

14. Which all-time great had an incredible 57-4 win/loss record in the Billie Jean King Cup?

15. Which country won the inaugural Billie Jean King Cup?

16. In what decade was the competition first held?

17. Which European country reached six straight Billie Jean Cup finals during the 1990s?

18. The first ever Billie Jean King Cup Final was hosted in which city? (Clue: It also hosts a Grand Slam event)

19. The Finals competition in the Billie Jean King Cup features how many countries? a) 8 b) 12 c) 16

20. How many countries entered the 2022 Billie Jean King Cup? a) 107 b) 117 c) 127

**Quiz 17: Answers**

1. Boris Becker 2. Slazenger 3. Ilie Nastase 4. Richard Gasquet 5. Sue Barker 6. Jimmy Connors 7. Vijay Amritraj 8. Andre Agassi 9. Roger Federer 10. Chris Evert 11. Bianca Andreescu 12. Billie Jean King 13. Conchita Martinez 14. Andre Agassi 15. John Isner 16. Ivo Karlovic 17. Andy Murray 18. Wimbledon 19. a) Bournemouth 20. a) 78 feet

## Quiz 19: Pot Luck

1. Who is the only man to win the BBC World Sports Star of the Year Award four times?

2. The Venus Rosewater Dish is a trophy awarded to the winner of which tournament?

3. Which of the four Grand Slam tournaments takes place earliest in the year?

4. The 2022 ATP Tour Finals were hosted in which Italian city?

5. In 1990, Andres Gomez became the first player from which South American country to win a Grand Slam singles title?

6. Who was the only male player to complete the career Grand Slam during the 1990s?

7. True or false – Rafa Nadal was unbeaten in games against Roger Federer played on clay?

8. Who was the first European man (and the second overall) to complete a career Grand Slam and also win an Olympic gold?

9. Who holds the record for appearing in the final of the same Men's Singles Major the most times without ever going on to win the tournament? (clue: it was the Australian Open)

10. How high in feet is the middle of a tennis net?

11. Which woman won the most Grand Slam singles titles during the 1980s?

12. Andy Murray won gold at the 2016 Rio Olympics after beating which Argentine in the final?

13. Which French Open winner and future coach of Rafa Nadal was the first Spanish man to be ranked number 1 in the ATP World Rankings?

14. Steffi Graf won the 1988 French Open in just 32 minutes, defeating which Belarusian opponent 6-0, 6-0?

15. True or false – Great Britain has appeared in the final of the Billie Jean King Cup four times and lost each time?

16. Complete the title of the best-selling book by US player turned coach, Brad Gilbert. 'Winning....'?

17. True or false – Two-time Grand Slam runner-up Andrea Jaeger became a nun following her tennis career?

18. Who is the only Austrian man to reach #1 in the ATP World Rankings?

19. How many players start the singles tournament at each of the four Majors? a) 64 b) 128 c) 256

20. On a tennis court, how far from the net is the service line? a) 19 feet b) 20 feet c) 21 feet

**Quiz 18: Answers**

1. USA 2. Switzerland 3. Glasgow 4. Arantxa Sanchez-Vicario 5. Margaret Court 6. Martina Navratilova 7. Czech Republic 8. Billie Jean King and Chris Evert 9. USA 10. Three 11. Martina Navratilova 12. Australia 13. False 14. Chris Evert 15. USA 16. 1960s 17. Spain 18. London 19. b) 12 countries 20. c) 127 countries

## Quiz 20: Wimbledon Firsts and Lasts

1. Who was the last man to win the Wimbledon Men's Singles title without dropping a set?

2. The last time the Ladies' Singles Final featured two players from the same country was 2009. Who were the two players involved?

3. Who was the last player other than Federer, Nadal, Murray or Djokovic to win the Wimbledon Men's Singles title?

4. Before Roger Federer, who was the last player to win the Men's Singles at Wimbledon whose full name starts and ends with the same letter?

5. Who was the last woman to win the Ladies' Singles, Ladies' Doubles and Mixed Doubles at Wimbledon in the same year?

6. Who was the first Spaniard to win the Ladies' Singles title at Wimbledon?

7. In what year were yellow balls used at Wimbledon for the first time?

8. What amazing feat happened for the first time at Wimbledon in 1984 and has never been repeated since?

9. Henry Billingham was the last player to regularly do what at Wimbledon?

10. Who was the last player to win the Men's Singles at Wimbledon whose first name and surname start with the same letter?

11. What member of the umpiring crew was introduced for the first time at the 1991 Wimbledon Championships?

12. In 2019, Simona Halep became the first woman from which country to win the Ladies' Singles at Wimbledon?

13. In what decade was Wimbledon broadcast on the radio for the first time?

14. Who was the first Czech player to win the Men's Singles at Wimbledon?

15. Who was the last teenager to win the Ladies' Singles Championship at Wimbledon?

16. Who was the last Briton to win the Wimbledon Ladies' Singles title?

17. In 2003, who became the first defending Wimbledon Men's Singles champion of the open era to lose in the opening match of the championship?

18. Who was the first Wimbledon champion to win a prize of £1 million? (clue: it was in 2010)

19. The first Wimbledon Championship took place in what year? a) 1877 b) 1887 c) 1897

20. In what year did gentlemen wear shorts at Wimbledon for the first time? a) 1920 b) 1930 c) 1940

**Quiz 19: Answers**

1. Roger Federer 2. Wimbledon Ladies' Singles 3. Australian Open 4. Turin 5. Ecuador 6. Andre Agassi 7. False 8. Rafa Nadal 9. Andy Murray 10. Three feet 11. Martina Navratilova 12. Juan Martin del Potro 13. Carlos Moya 14. Natasha Zvereva 15. True 16. Ugly 17. True 18. Thomas Muster 19. b) 128 players 20. c) 21 feet

## Quiz 21: Pot Luck

1. Inspired by ancient myth, what was the name of the device introduced in 1980 to act as an electronic line-judge?

2. Which of the four Grand Slams takes place latest in the year?

3. Between 2009 and 2020 the ATP Finals event was hosted in which city?

4. Which of the Williams sisters is older – Serena or Venus?

5. Andy Murray defeated which opponent to claim the 2012 U.S. Open title?

6. Who are the two players in the open era to win five straight Wimbledon Men's Singles titles?

7. Since the start of the open era, which country has provided the most Men's Singles Major winners?

8. Who is the oldest woman to be ranked the world's number one singles player?

9. Who is the only male player to have won more than 70 titles in both singles and doubles events?

10. Bianca Andreescu was the first player from which country to win a Grand Slam singles title?

11. What three-word phrase is said by the umpire to indicate the contest is over and a player has won?

12. Which 46-year-old was one half of a Wimbledon Mixed Doubles-winning partnership in 2003?

13. Which American star made a cameo appearance in the 2011 Adam Sandler / Jennifer Aniston comedy 'Just Go With it', credited as 'The Good-Looking Guy on a Plane'?

14. Balls are changed in ATP tournaments after how many games?

15. True or false – At least every edition of Wimbledon has been interrupted by rain at least once?

16. Whose 15 Men's Singles Major championship wins during the 2010s were the most by any player during that decade?

17. Which of the four Majors attracts the largest aggregate number of spectators?

18. Who are the two South American men to reach #1 in the ATP World Rankings?

19. What is the name of the Wimbledon hawk that makes sure that pigeons don't interrupt play? a) Humphrey b) Rufus c) Sherlock

20. Wimbledon is famously located in which postal district? a) SW1 b) SW9 c) SW19

**Quiz 20: Answers**

1. Roger Federer 2. Venus and Serena Williams 3. Lleyton Hewitt 4. Rod Laver 5. Billie Jean King 6. Conchita Martinez 7. 1986 8. All five titles were won by the defending champion 9. Serve underarm 10. Andre Agassi 11. Net cord monitor 12. Romania 13. 1920s 14. Jan Kodeš 15. Maria Sharapova 16. Virginia Wade 17. Lleyton Hewitt 18. Rafa Nadal 19. a) 1877 20. b) 1930

## Quiz 22: Anagrams (Men)

Rearrange the letters to make the name of a Major-winning male tennis player.

1. Alan Farad

2. Pampas Trees

3. Vodka Vino Jock

4. Army Run Day

5. Airs Agendas

6. Dr Org Referee

7. Grandest Beef

8. Alas Coral Czar

9. Cap Hats

10. Conjoin My Mrs

11. Rave Lord

12. Twins Alarmed

13. Vision Raving Ace

14. Hot Mini Medic

15. Irk Card Hijacker

16. Dockyard Din

17. Antigua Goods

18. This Chemical

19. Yank On Chain

20. Village Rum Silo

**Quiz 21: Answers**

1. Cyclops 2. U.S. Open 3. London 4. Venus 5. Novak Djokovic 6. Bjorn Borg and Roger Federer 7. USA 8. Serena Williams 9. John McEnroe 10. Canada 11. 'Game, set, match' 12. Martina Navratilova 13. Andy Roddick 14. After the first seven games then after every ninth game 15. False 16. Novak Djokovic 17. Australian Open 18. Marcelo Rios and Gustavo Kuerton 19. b) Rufus 20. c) SW19

## Quiz 23: Pot Luck

1. The Suzanne Lenglen Trophy is awarded to the winner of which tournament?

2. Who is the only British player to reach number 1 in the ATP Rankings?

3. Indian Wells, the venue for a famous event on the men's and women's tours, is in which American state?

4. Which tennis player was voted the most stylish man of the 2010s by readers of GQ Magazine?

5. Who was the first player to win the gold medal at the Olympic Men's Singles Tennis more than once?

6. In 2021, who became just the second man in the open era to win the Australian Open, the French Open and Wimbledon in the same season?

7. Which player won the most Men's Singles Majors throughout the 1990s?

8. True or false – When first introduced, tiebreakers at Wimbledon were played when the score reached 8 games all?

9. Andy Murray has reached one French Open final. Who beat the Scot in the 2016 decider?

10. Who won more Major singles titles – Jimmy Connors or John McEnroe?

11. What is the fewest number of points required to win a set in tennis?

12. Strawberries and cream are traditionally associated with which Major?

13. What is traditionally the final event played on Centre Court at the Wimbledon Championships?

14. 'Superbrat' was the nickname of which player?

15. Which former U.S. tennis number 1 and Davis Cup captain made his debut on golf's PGA Tour at the 2022 3M Open in Minnesota?

16. True or false – The oldest player to appear in a Davis Cup match was 66 years old?

17. Which woman won her first Major at the 49th attempt in 2015, the longest stretch before a maiden win in the women's game?

18. Before Andy Murray, who was the last British man to win a Major Men's Singles title?

19. In what year was the Hawkeye line-judging technology first used at Wimbledon? a) 2002 b) 2007 c) 2012

20. At the 1997 Wimbledon Championships, Pete Sampras served 118 games. How of those games did he win? a) 114 b) 116 c) 118

**Quiz 22: Answers**

1. Rafa Nadal 2. Pete Sampras 3. Novak Djokovic 4. Andy Murray 5. Andre Agassi 6. Roger Federer 7. Stefan Edberg 8. Carlos Alcaraz 9. Pat Cash 10. Jimmy Connors 11. Rod Laver 12. Mats Wilander 13. Goran Ivanisevic 14. Dominic Thiem 15. Richard Krajicek 16. Andy Roddick 17. Gaston Gaudio 18. Michael Stich 19. Yannick Noah 20. Guillermo Vilas

## Quiz 24: Anagrams

Rearrange the letters to make the name of a female Major winner.

1. Fits Gaffer

2. Chit Server

3. Tag Sea Kiwi

4. Nail

5. Hasty Bar

6. Naval Tram Variation

7. A Real Smile Wins

8. Hi Mint Sangria

9. Iceman Loses

10. Army Recipe

11. Villa Muse Wins

12. Manorial Orbit

13. Tarmac Tore Rug

14. Enthuse Jinni

15. Private Oak TV

16. Deadpan Vinyl Sort

17. Enquire Leg Break

18. Aviation Rake Czar

19. Animals Hope

20. A Caravans Zen Taxi Choir

**Quiz 23: Answers**

1. French Open Women's Singles 2. Andy Murray 3. California 4. Roger Federer 5. Andy Murray 6. Novak Djokovic 7. Pete Sampras 8. True 9. Novak Djokovic 10. Jimmy Connors 11. 24 points 12. Wimbledon 13. Ladies' Doubles Final 14. John McEnroe 15. Mardy Fish 16. True 17. Flavia Pennetta 18. Fred Perry 19. b) 2007 20. b) 116 games

## Quiz 25: Pot Luck

1. The winner of which tournament receives The Daphne Akhurst Memorial Trophy?

2. What is the name of the annual men's competition that pits a team from Europe against a team from the rest of the world?

3. Who was the last Australian to win the Men's Singles at the Australian Open?

4. Who are the two British male tennis players to have won the BBC Sports Personality of the Year Award?

5. A hilly viewing terrace at Wimbledon is informally named after which British player?

6. Who are the two players to appear in the Men's Singles at Wimbledon for 22 straight tournaments?

7. Who has appeared in the most Men's Singles Major finals since the start of the open era?

8. Which woman won the most Grand Slam singles titles during the 1990s?

9. Stefanos Tsitsipas was the first man from which country to reach a Grand Slam final?

10. True or false – The Australian Open has previously been hosted in Adelaide?

11. Is the first point of a game always served from the left or right-hand side of the court?

12. Which country lost four Davis Cup finals between 1981 and 2011 before winning their first title in 2016?

13. True or false – The 2022 Women's PGA Golf Champion Nelly Korda is the daughter of 1998 Australian Open tennis winner Petr Korda?

14. Which two-time Major-winning Russian later tried his hand at golf and also cashed multiple times at the World Series of Poker?

15. Who holds the record for the most weeks as the world's number 1 male player in the ATP World Rankings by an American?

16. Which all-time great was part of a record six Grand Slam-winning men's doubles partnerships during the 1980s?

17. In 1977, three British brothers from which family all took part in the Men's Singles at Wimbledon?

18. True or false – 'Tennis balls' are mentioned in William Shakespeare's 'Henry V'?

19. Between 2003 and 2005 Roger Federer won how many consecutive finals he appeared in? a) 20 b) 22 c) 24

20. The fastest serve ever recorded at Wimbledon was delivered in 2010 by America's Taylor Dent. What speed was that serve? a) 144mph b) 146mph c) 148mph

**Quiz 24: Answers**

1. Steffi Graf 2. Chris Evert 3. Iga Swiatek 4. Li Na 5. Ash Barty 6. Martina Navratilova 7. Serena Williams 8. Martina Hingis 9. Monica Seles 10. Mary Pierce 11. Venus Williams 12. Marion Bartoli 13. Margaret Court 14. Justine Henin 15. Petra Kvitova 16. Lindsay Davenport 17. Angelique Kerber 18. Victoria Azarenka 19. Simona Halep 20. Arantxa Sánchez Vicario

**Other Titles in the Sports Quiz Books series include:**

Formula One Trivia Quiz Book
MotoGP Trivia Quiz Book
Golf Trivia Quiz Book
Boston Red Sox Trivia Quiz Book
Chicago Cubs Trivia Quiz Book
New York Yankees Trivia Quiz Book
Baltimore Ravens Trivia Quiz Book
Chicago Bears Trivia Quiz Book
Cincinnati Bengals Trivia Quiz Book
Dallas Cowboys Trivia Quiz Book
Denver Broncos Trivia Quiz Book
Green Bay Packers Trivia Quiz Book
Kansas City Chiefs Trivia Quiz Book
Miami Dolphins Trivia Quiz Book
Minnesota Vikings Trivia Quiz Book
New England Patriots Trivia Quiz Book
New York Giants Trivia Quiz Book
Philadelphia Eagles Trivia Quiz Book
Pittsburgh Steelers Trivia Quiz Book
San Francisco 49ers Trivia Quiz Book
Seattle Seahawks Trivia Quiz Book
Tampa Bay Buccaneers Trivia Quiz Book
Washington Commanders Trivia Quiz Book
Georgia Bulldogs Trivia Quiz Book
Michigan Wolverines Trivia Quiz Book

Made in the USA
Coppell, TX
22 November 2024

40794005R10038